D1546328

WINNING *is* PLANNED

A Guide for Young Men Who Plan Their Greatness

Dr. Stanley K. Ellis & Dr. Jessica K. Ellis

SILLE
EDUCATIONAL CONSULTING

First Printing, 2020
ISBN 978-0-578-77265-3
P.O. Box 165032
Little Rock, AR 72116
www.mie4success.org

Then the LORD answered me and said:
"Write the vision and make it plain on tablets,
That he may run who reads it.
For the vision is yet for an appointed time...

HABAKUK 2:2-3

I am happy that you have chosen to pick this journal up or that someone who cares about you has placed it in your hands. If it is the latter, consider it a gift from someone who wants to help you propel your life and fertilize your prosperity. If it is the former, then I applaud you for your courage to engage with such a book and I encourage you to be diligent, steadfast, and true to the work that you do inside these pages... and *inside your mind.*

This book has been developed to help you define your Success, to Motivate you, to Inspire you, and to Empower you to achieve whatever goals you set for yourself. Just like most things in life that are worth attaining, Success is a process. To enjoy your Success, you have to enjoy the process. I like to call it the M.I.E. process. To help you understand what you should be doing here in this journal and why you should be doing it, let us begin by defining Success and the process of **M**otivation, **I**nspiration, and **E**mpowerment that will get you there.

Success in 66:

We all have habits. Some of them are good and some are not so good. Some of our habits we are very proud of and others, well, not so much. What I would like for you to realize at this point in your journal is that none of your not-so-good habits will help you achieve the Success you want and deserve. Brace yourself! Some of your good habits won't help you achieve your Success either. See, just because the habit is "good" does not mean that it will help you achieve your goals. To achieve your goals, the habits you build MUST be focused on and lead to the Success you desire. For example: You have a habit of swimming 5 miles each day. However, your goal is to one day be a world-class skateboarder. Your good habit of swimming 5 miles WILL NOT lead to you becoming a skateboard champion. Your habits have to be focused towards your goals for you to achieve them.

Some experts say that it takes 66 days to develop a habit. Other experts tell us that to become Successful, we have to develop good habits and get rid of bad habits (or learn to manage them better). In essence, you are here to develop good behaviors that will become natural to you. You will begin to do these things with the regularity and consistency that you exhibit with simple things like brushing your teeth, tying your shoes or combing your hair. Okay, maybe combing your hair takes a little more thought, but you get the picture. I have developed this journal you currently hold in your hand to help you start your journey to Success. This journal will help you build good habits… **in 66 days**… that focus directly on you achieving your goals.

The Look of Success:

Everyone defines Success differently. Some see Success as having a lot of money, while other see it as having a big house or fancy car. Many think that they will have achieved "Success" when they accomplish or achieve the goal that they have set for themselves. In actuality, none of these things define what Success really is. Most people see Success as a destination. A place you get to and stop. In all actuality, Success is *the pursuit of a worthy goal*. Success comes from going after what it is you want. Success is the process. To be truly Successful, you must learn to enjoy the process, the pursuit of your goals. If you cannot learn to be happy while you are going after your goal, you will not be happy when you reach it. Let us be clear, if you have a worthy goal and you are going after it, you are already Successful. If you learn to enjoy the pursuit of your goal, your happiness will last much longer than when you reach it. The first step is to identify your Motivation.

The Truth About Motivation:

Most people think motivation is the excitement you get or feel about your goal. People often confuse motivation with feeling good or being excited about something. Feeling good and being excited is something else altogether. I will explain what I mean in the next paragraph. For now, let us focus on Motivation.

Motivation is your reason for having your goal in the first place. Your goal may be to have a really big house one day. Your reason could be you want to give your mother the home she never had, or perhaps you want to take care of all your sisters and brothers, or maybe a big house says to you that you have "made it". Your motivation is *your reason, your why*. Identifying "why" you want to achieve this goal is your motivation. This is your anchor. When times get hard (**and they will**) on your journey to achieving your goal, your motivation, your why will be what keeps you going. Your why is what makes the goal worth achieving in the first place. Step two is to keep yourself Inspired.

Keeping Yourself Going:

You should certainly *have a goal that you are excited about, have enthusiasm for achieving the goal and feel good when you are working towards it.* This is what inspiration is. The truth of the matter is that your inspiration will come and go, but your motivation, your "why", is the anchor that keeps you going even when you do not feel like it. People think when you are excited and fired up about your goal, you are motivated. That is not true. Those feelings are your Inspiration. They are as necessary as your motivation. Both your motivation and your inspiration are part of a formula that will help you on your journey **of** Success. You should always try to stay inspired about your goal. Feeling good about it makes the journey that much more enjoyable but inspiration is NOT a constant. It is not always there. Stay inspired as much as you can. You must Inspire and re-Inspire yourself each day. The third step is to Empower yourself.

Authorizing Your Own Success:

Empowerment is utilizing the resources at your disposal, the tools you have acquired as well as the knowledge and experiences you have gained to help you achieve your goals. Empowerment is also, *you authorizing yourself to achieve your goals*. Empowerment is you telling yourself that you have the right to the Success that you desire. This is probably the most important part of empowerment. You have to give yourself the authority to be Successful. Only you can authorize your Success and only you can take that authorization away. You are in control. You will either empower yourself or you will dis-empower yourself. The first one will ensure your Success. The second will ensure your UN-Success. The final step in the Success process is to **REPEAT** steps one, two and three.

Steven Covey, author of *The 7 Habits of Highly Effective People*, stated that you should begin with the end in mind. You need to know where you are going before you can plan your journey, otherwise you end up travelling without an actual destination. If you do this, you are wasting your time and could end up anywhere. This is not the route you will want to take. To be effective in planning to achieve your goal and Successful in reaching your destination, you will have to identify the steps between where you are right now in your life and where you want to be. There will be a lot of mini-goals or steps you will have to make before you achieve the Success goal you have identified for yourself. No man, no team, nobody wins without a plan. How well you plan will determine how fast and how much Success you enjoy. The main thing to remember is this, to achieve your Success you will have to become the person who would deserve that Success. You will have to change to become the person you are meant to be. You will have to change how you think, how you act, how you talk and perhaps how you look so that who you are lines up with who you are meant to be.

No Success will ever come to you without change on your part in some area or multiple areas of your life. The change will not always feel good but it will be necessary to achieve your goals. One of these changes may require you to seek out new friends and probably leave some of your older ones behind. You will need to seek out new information from new people. This will be scary but you will need to overcome your fear to achieve your goal. Not all around you will understand why you are changing or why you even want Success. This will be a major source of discomfort for you, but once again, it will be necessary for you to become who you are meant to be and achieve the Success you deserve. You will need to make your change part of your plan to win.

If you do not plan to win, you are planning to fail. To achieve any great Success in life you must begin with your goal in mind and lay out your plan to achieve that goal. You can look at it this way, if you were going on a trip to a different state you would plan your route to get there. Part of your plan would include buying snacks, filling your car with gas, identifying places you may stop for food along the way and places you may stop to sleep. All of this would be done before you ever leave your home. It is all planned as part of your journey to get to your destination. This is no different from planning to achieve your Success in life. You MUST layout your plan or shall I say, write your plan out. A plan that is not written down is simply a thought. Thoughts are often forgotten and so are the plans that are contained in those thoughts. Writing your plans down on paper helps you keep them in your mind and gives you something to refer back to if you can not remember exactly what you said you were going to do. Written plans can also keep you inspired as you work on achieving your goal. Just seeing your goals and plans written down on paper can give you something you can get excited about and fuel you to push forward, especially when you do not feel like it. Just like any other journey, when things happen and you have to get off the road to fix a flat or get more fuel, your plan is there to tell you which direction to go when you get back on the road. Things will happen in your life that may take you off the road to your goals for a moment but your plan is there to help you get back on the path to complete your journey and achieve YOUR SUCCESS.

Habakkuk 2:2—Write the vision and make it plain on tablets.

Many people talk about the sacrifices they make as if they should be praised for them. Parents are in this group. Sometimes parents like to talk about the number of sacrifices they have made for their children. Nine times out of 10 they are telling this to their children and they want praise for what they have sacrificed. Sometimes parents do not see what they have sacrificed as positive investments into their children's lives, futures and ultimately their Success. This is probably where the cycle of seeing the things you do in your life to succeed as sacrifices (negative) and not investments (positive).

Most people see what they do to become Successful as sacrifice. If they save their money to buy real estate, purchase stock in the stock market, or start a business, you will hear them say, "I sacrificed to do this". Really what they are considering a sacrifice should be viewed as an INVESTMENT towards achieving the Success they want. Today, as you read this book and begin your work on your goals, I encourage you to see everything you do to achieve your goals as an INVESTMENT that is getting you one step closer to the Success you want and deserve. As Success Seekers, everything we do is an investment. Nothing we do is a sacrifice.

Denying ourselves of anything that we currently want just so we can have the Success we know is down the road is an INVESTMENT. When you skip getting something you want now to reach your goals later, I want you to say this to yourself: **"Everything I do is an INVESTMENT. Nothing I do is a sacrifice. I am WINNING. I am Successful."**

How you view your actions and behaviors is just as important as how you act and behave. To reach your goals, to achieve the Success you have identified for yourself, you must first change how you see and think about things. Our perspective, our view of things is what sometimes keeps us from reaching our goals. It is so very important that you adjust your view of things to see yourself as Successful and WINNING in all that you do. Changing your mindset is an INVESTMENT in itself—probably the most important one you will ever make. It is an INVESTMENT in you.

It would be very wrong of me to get you started on this journey without discussing one of the most important resources that you have at your fingertips and how you should use it. That resource is **TIME**. We all have the same 24 hours in a day, the same 52 weeks in a year and the same 365 days in that year. We receive lots of advice about how we should manage our time and there are numerous strategies that will help us do it. When we are told how to manage our time, we are told to do things that are "constructive". Being "constructive" is important and doing so is probably a good use of our time and a good strategy for managing it. What is often overlooked is whether your "constructive" use of time is you maxing the use of your time. Maxing your time is you making the most of the time you have with your constructive activities and ensuring that those activities are ALL focused on achieving your goals. You can manage your time well, you can be constructive and yet none of your actions may be focused towards you achieving your Success. When all of your actions and all of your time is focused on reaching your goals then you are *Time Maxing*. Time Maxing is your goal when it comes to your time. Simply managing your time is not enough. You should be so focused on achieving your goals that if you can not see how an activity fits into you achieving your goals you replace that activity with another one that is linked to you reaching your Success. To be Successful do not simply manage your time, MAX IT.

Within these pages you will find quotes from various literary works, including the Holy Bible, and other life and self-improvement teachings by famous and not so famous people, all of which I expect you to use for your elevation and for you to assist others in elevating themselves.

Let us begin with this Bible verse...in Galatians 5:22 God says, "But the fruit of the Spirit is love, joy, peace, <u>longsuffering</u>, gentleness, goodness, faith." I think it is important for us to address the underlined word in this statement before we go further. Without referencing Webster's Dictionary or the Internet, we know and understand that the word "*long*" means that something has a stretched out existence. And then, God says to us that this stretched out existence will be composed of *suffering*, which equates to *hardships, despair, trouble, uncomfortableness, work, tiredness, uneasiness, bad times——* things that you will be unhappy about and maybe even cause you mental and/or physical discomfort.

However, Jesus also said in John 10:10, "I have come that you may have life, and that you may have *it* more abundantly". Essentially, this statement tells us that it is our **divine** right to live a good life, to enjoy life, to have as much as we would like from life. These two statements together tell us one thing; our Success **WILL NOT** come without some bad times. **But,** if we will endure the bad times, we will earn our Success, which is waiting for us at the other end.

To say it bluntly, bad times are part of the process. You will have to stop at failure on your road to Success, but you don't have to stay there. So, to help you navigate your way to your Success with the least number of failure stops along the way, I have developed this journal for you. As you go through it, you will first write down your main life goal. This will be what you want most out of life. Understand that this DOES NOT have to be only one thing. You can have two main goals or Two Plan A's, as I like to call them. You are not limited to what you can do or the Success you can have. But, you MUST plan for any Success you expect. Next, write down the things that will help you reach your biggest goals. These are your intermediate or midpoint goals. Your midpoint goals help you to realize small wins through your journey that will keep you Inspired. Third, write down the things that let you know you are making progress towards achieving your goals. You will measure your success by these three things. Afterwards, write down the investments you will make in yourself that will ensure you achieve the Success you want and deserve.

Wait! You're not done yet. To ensure you get what you want out of this journal you have to commit to writing in it each day. (If you miss a day, that is okay...JUST DO NOT MISS TWO DAYS IN A ROW.) You want to build a habit of writing down daily goals each day, tracking your Success towards achieving them, and reflecting on your progress in the evening--each evening. Once this process is part of your daily behaviors and becomes a habit for you, you will be much closer to your Success.

Here are examples that will help you as you fill in your daily activities and accomplishments.

STEP 1

Write out your biggest goal for your future.

I call this your long-term goal. It will normally take some time before you reach this goal but it is very important for you to have. If you find it hard to write this out, think of it this way... if you could make a million dollars *doing whatever you wanted*, what would you do? Nothing that you can think of and no idea you might have is too silly here. Just write it down.

▶ My Biggest Goal for My Future is/is to:

Be a video game designer for E.A. Sports.

Great! You have just completed the first step in achieving Success for yourself. Do not worry if your goal is not perfect. You can come back and make it better later. The next thing you will need to do is take the second step on this journey.

STEP 2

Write down the top three things that you will first need to do to help you achieve your goal(s).

These three things are what we like to call your short-term goals. If this is hard to understand think of it this way, if your main goal was to eat an entire pizza, you could not do it by placing the whole thing in your mouth at one time. You would have to eat slice one, slice two, slice three…until you had eaten the whole pizza. In this case, your main goal (*long-term goal*) is the entire pizza and each slice of the pizza is a *short-term goal* to help you get there. Now that you understand that, go ahead and write down the **top three things you need to do within the next year (12 months) to reach your long-term goal.** These three things could also be behaviors that you may need to change to help you reach your goal. It is always good to ask others who you respect to help you with this step. I suggest you talk to your parents, teachers, pastor, or even principal. Trust me, they will certainly be impressed that you asked them to help you with this question and will probably be thrilled to give you good advice.

1. Graduate High School.
....

....

2. Apply to a school that has a video
....
   game design program.
....

3. Read 12 books on a video game
....
   design concept.
....

Now that you have completed Step 2, you will need to make sure you can measure your Success.

STEP 3

Write down at least three different ways you will be able to tell if you are on track to meet your goals.

Let me give you an example. If your long-term goal is to go to college, one way to measure your progress towards achieving your goal might be to graduate from high school. Another measure of your progress may be to apply for college or take the ACT exam. These are all things that will help you achieve your long-term goal of going to college. Write down three ways you will measure your progress.

1. Submit applications to 3 game design programs.
....

2. Read one game design book each month.
....

....

3. Post twice a week to a game design blog/ chat room.
....

Please understand how important it is for you to establish ways for you to measure your Success. You need to know that you are doing well and making good progress in achieving your goals. This will help keep you inspired about the direction you are going in and provide you with more fuel for your forward movement.

Step 4 is just as important as Step 1. In this step, you take responsibility or increase your responsibility in achieving your Success. You must keep in mind that **your Success is your responsibility**...no one else's. Taking responsibility for your own Success will require you to do some things you may not already be doing. How you spend your time may be something you consider changing. Also, you may have to educate yourself about things you don't already know about that will help you succeed. You will certainly need to find a mentor...more than one. Regardless of what anyone tells you, nobody has ever succeeded on their own. Those who are really Successful will more than likely tell you they had a mentor or someone who showed them the way. If you haven't already guessed it, mentors are very important to your Success.

STEP 4

Finish the following statements with your own answers.

A. I will make time for my Success by:

> Scheduling time to read 10 pages a day about game design.

B. I will increase my knowledge about:

> Video game character development.

C. I will ask the following people to advise/ mentor me:

1. Mr. Marks
....

2. Ms. Loti
....

3. Ms. Ash
....

EVENING REFLECTION

► The single most important thing I did today to get me closer to my goals was:

> Contact Dr. Johnson at the College of Game Design.

► The one thing that hurt my progress the most today was:

> Choosing to watch T.V. instead of getting my friends to subscribe to my Youtube channel.

► I will overcome this obstacle tomorrow by:

> Getting my friends to subscribe to my You-tube channel instead of watching T.V.

5-DAY ACCOUNTABILITY CHECK

During the past 5 days...

▶ I made time for my success by:

> Making sure I read at least 10 pages each day.

▶ I increased my knowledge about:

> graphics in character design.

▶ I asked for advice/guidance from:

Ms. Ash

....

....

....

▶ Over the next 5 days I will talk with/communicate with Mr./Ms./Dr ...Ellis.................. about:

> my goals.

1. Identify your **Two Plan A's**

Quite often when young people describe their goals to adults, those adults might respond by saying, "What is your plan b?" or "What is your fall back plan?" This type of thinking is absolutely WRONG. The problem with a plan b or a fall back plan is that once it is introduced to you and you decide to adopt these secondary plan concepts, you immediately accept the fact that you can fail. You immediately give life to the possibility that you will not achieve your goals. So right here and right now, I need you to decide that you will not have a plan b nor will you have a fall back plan. Do not accept failure. INSTEAD, why not have Two Plan A's?

Having Two Plan A's is very different from having a plan b or a fall back plan. Having Two Plan A's is you choosing to succeed in more than one thing. Everyone has more in them than they believe they do and certainly more than they are comfortable with doing. Everyone is interested in doing more than one thing. When you elect to have Two Plan A's you are deciding to be great at more than one thing. With this idea in mind,

I have developed this journal specifically for you to pursue and achieve both of your Plan A's. So why don't you flip to the next page and begin the process to achieve the Success you want and deserve. It is my firm belief that before you start to pursue your Success, there are several steps that you must take. The first step is to identify the goal you want to achieve. No one in the history of being Successful has ever achieved their Success without identifying a goal and an endpoint. Most of us have goals in mind or things we want to achieve in life. Sometimes we are not able to state our goals clearly. That is okay though. To help with this, I have an exercise I want you to try.

STEP 1

Write out your biggest goal for your future.

I call this your long-term goal. It will normally take some time before you reach this goal but it is very important for you to have. If you find it hard to write this out, think of it this way... if you could make a million dollars *doing whatever you wanted*, what would you do? Nothing that you can think of and no idea you might have is too silly here. Just write it down.

▶ My Biggest Goal for My Future is/is to:

Great! You have just completed the first step in achieving Success for yourself. Do not worry if your goal is not perfect. You can come back and make it better later. The next thing you will need to do is take the second step on this journey.

STEP 2

Write down the top three things that you will first need to do to help you achieve your goal(s).

These three things are what we like to call your short-term goals. If this is hard to understand think of it this way, if your main goal was to eat an entire pizza, you could not do it by placing the whole thing in your mouth at one time. You would have to eat slice one, slice two, slice three…until you had eaten the whole pizza. In this case, your main goal (*long-term goal*) is the entire pizza and each slice of the pizza is a *short-term goal* to help you get there. Now that you understand that, go ahead and write down the **top three things you need to do within the next year (12 months) to reach your long-term goal.** These three things could also be behaviors that you may need to change to help you reach your goal. It is always good to ask others who you respect to help you with this step. I suggest you talk to your parents, teachers, pastor, or even principal. Trust me, they will certainly be impressed that you asked them to help you with this question and will probably be thrilled to give you good advice.

1.
....

....

2.
....

....

3.
....

....

Now that you have completed Step 2, you will need to make sure you can measure your Success.

STEP 3

Write down at least three different ways you will be able to tell if you are on track to meet your goals.

Let me give you an example. If your long-term goal is to go to college, one way to measure your progress towards achieving your goal might be to graduate from high school. Another measure of your progress may be to apply for college or take the ACT exam. These are all things that will help you achieve your long-term goal of going to college. Write down three ways you will measure your progress.

1.
....

....

2.
....

....

3.
....

....

Please understand how important it is for you to establish ways for you to measure your Success. You need to know that you are doing well and making good progress in achieving your goals. This will help keep you inspired about the direction you are going in and provide you with more fuel for your forward movement.

Step 4 is just as important as Step 1. In this step, you take responsibility or increase your responsibility in achieving your Success. You must keep in mind that **your Success is your responsibility**...no one else's. Taking responsibility for your own Success will require you to do some things you may not already be doing. How you spend your time may be something you consider changing. Also, you may have to educate yourself about things you don't already know about that will help you succeed. You will certainly need to find a mentor...more than one. Regardless of what anyone tells you, nobody has ever succeeded on their own. Those who are really Successful will more than likely tell you they had a mentor or someone who showed them the way. If you haven't already guessed it, mentors are very important to your Success.

STEP 4

Finish the following statements with your own answers.

D. I will make time for my Success by:

E. I will increase my knowledge about:

F. I will ask the following people to advise/
    mentor me:

....

....

....

3 BOOKS TO READ FOR MOTIVATION

- ► *The Wealthy Gardner* by John Soforic
- ► *The Richest Man in Babylon*
  by George S. Clason
- ► *The Magic of Thinking Big* by David Schwartz

"Fear is the devil trying to keep you from your Success."
—**Dr. S.K. Ellis,** *Investor & Entrepreneur*

MORNING PLANNING

▶ I choose to have joy today because:

▶ I am working towards my goal because:

My Plan A. is:

....

....

► The **first** thing I will do today to get me closer to achieving my Plan A. is:

Start Time: .... End Time: ....

► The **second** thing I will do today to get me closer to achieving my Plan A. is:

Start Time: .... End Time: ....

My next plan A is:

....

....

► The **first** thing I will do today to get me closer to achieving my next Plan A is:

Start Time: .... End Time: ....

► The **second** thing I will do today to get me closer to achieving my next Plan A is:

Start Time: .... End Time: ....

► Today, I will talk with/communicate with Mr./ Ms./Dr. .... about:

EVENING REFLECTION

► The single most important thing I did today to get me closer to my goals was:

► The one thing that hurt my progress the most today was:

► I will overcome this obstacle tomorrow by:

"Every Sunday needs a plan...and so does Monday, Tuesday, Wednesday, Thursday, Friday, and Saturday."

—Dr. S.K. Ellis, *Investor & Entrepreneur*

MORNING PLANNING

► I choose to have joy today because:

► I am working towards my goal because:

My Plan A. is:

....

....

► The **first** thing I will do today to get me closer to achieving my Plan A. is:

Start Time: .... End Time: ....

► The **second** thing I will do today to get me closer to achieving my Plan A. is:

Start Time: .... End Time: ....

My next plan A is:

....

....

► The **first** thing I will do today to get me closer to achieving my next Plan A is:

Start Time: .... End Time: ....

► The **second** thing I will do today to get me closer to achieving my next Plan A is:

Start Time: .... End Time: ....

► Today, I will talk with/communicate with Mr./ Ms./Dr. .... about:

EVENING REFLECTION

► The single most important thing I did today to get me closer to my goals was:

► The one thing that hurt my progress the most today was:

► I will overcome this obstacle tomorrow by:

"An excuse is a door that swings open to your UN-Success. Close that door and open a different one."

—**DR. S.K. ELLIS,** *Investor & Entrepreneur*

MORNING PLANNING

► I choose to have joy today because:

► I am working towards my goal because:

My Plan A. is:

....

....

► The **first** thing I will do today to get me closer to achieving my Plan A. is:

Start Time: .... End Time: ....

► The **second** thing I will do today to get me closer to achieving my Plan A. is:

Start Time: .... End Time: ....

My next plan A is:

....

....

► The **first** thing I will do today to get me closer to achieving my next Plan A is:

Start Time: .... End Time: ....

► The **second** thing I will do today to get me closer to achieving my next Plan A is:

Start Time: .... End Time: ....

► Today, I will talk with/communicate with Mr./Ms./Dr. .... about:

EVENING REFLECTION

▶ The single most important thing I did today to get me closer to my goals was:

▶ The one thing that hurt my progress the most today was:

▶ I will overcome this obstacle tomorrow by:

DAY 4, Date:

Increase your actions to match your expectations and the Universe will increase its reciprocation.

—DR. S.K. ELLIS, *Investor & Entrepreneur*

MORNING PLANNING

► I choose to have joy today because:

► I am working towards my goal because:

My Plan A. is:

....

....

► The **first** thing I will do today to get me closer to achieving my Plan A. is:

Start Time: .... End Time: ....

► The **second** thing I will do today to get me closer to achieving my Plan A. is:

Start Time: .... End Time: ....

My next plan A is:

....

....

► The **first** thing I will do today to get me closer to achieving my next Plan A is:

Start Time: .... End Time: ....

► The **second** thing I will do today to get me closer to achieving my next Plan A is:

Start Time: .... End Time: ....

► Today, I will talk with/communicate with Mr./ Ms./Dr. .... about:

EVENING REFLECTION

► The single most important thing I did today to get me closer to my goals was:

► The one thing that hurt my progress the most today was:

► I will overcome this obstacle tomorrow by:

The first act of courage is to acknowledge that you are afraid. The second is to act anyway.

—Dr. S.K. Ellis, *Investor & Entrepreneur*

MORNING PLANNING

► I choose to have joy today because:

► I am working towards my goal because:

My Plan A. is:

....

....

► The **first** thing I will do today to get me closer to achieving my Plan A. is:

Start Time: .... End Time: ....

► The **second** thing I will do today to get me closer to achieving my Plan A. is:

Start Time: .... End Time: ....

My next plan A is:

....

....

► The **first** thing I will do today to get me closer to achieving my next Plan A is:

Start Time: .... End Time: ....

► The **second** thing I will do today to get me closer to achieving my next Plan A is:

Start Time: .... End Time: ....

► Today, I will talk with/communicate with Mr./ Ms./Dr. .... about:

EVENING REFLECTION

▶ The single most important thing I did today to get me closer to my goals was:

▶ The one thing that hurt my progress the most today was:

▶ I will overcome this obstacle tomorrow by:

5-DAY ACCOUNTABILITY CHECK

During the past 5 days...

▶ I made time for my success by:

▶ I increased my knowledge about:

▶ I asked for advice/guidance from:

....

....

....

▶ Over the next 5 days I will talk with/communicate
with Mr./Ms./Dr. .... about:

Use your setbacks as stepping-stones instead of tombstones.

—DR. S.K. ELLIS, *Investor & Entrepreneur*

MORNING PLANNING

▶ I choose to have joy today because:

▶ I am working towards my goal because:

My Plan A. is:

....

....

► The **first** thing I will do today to get me closer to achieving my Plan A. is:

Start Time: .... End Time: ....

► The **second** thing I will do today to get me closer to achieving my Plan A. is:

Start Time: .... End Time: ....

My next plan A is:

....

....

► The **first** thing I will do today to get me closer to achieving my next Plan A is:

Start Time: .... End Time: ....

► The **second** thing I will do today to get me closer to achieving my next Plan A is:

Start Time: .... End Time: ....

► Today, I will talk with/communicate with Mr./Ms./Dr. .... about:

EVENING REFLECTION

► The single most important thing I did today to get me closer to my goals was:

► The one thing that hurt my progress the most today was:

► I will overcome this obstacle tomorrow by:

"There are 5 D's to Success. Be Definite. Be Deliberate. Be Diligent. Be Determined. Be Damned if you do not win."

—**DR. S.K. ELLIS,** *Investor & Entrepreneur*

MORNING PLANNING

► I choose to have joy today because:

► I am working towards my goal because:

My Plan A. is:

....

....

► The **first** thing I will do today to get me closer to achieving my Plan A. is:

Start Time: .... End Time: ....

► The **second** thing I will do today to get me closer to achieving my Plan A. is:

Start Time: .... End Time: ....

My next plan A is:

....

....

► The **first** thing I will do today to get me closer to achieving my next Plan A is:

Start Time: .... End Time: ....

► The **second** thing I will do today to get me closer to achieving my next Plan A is:

Start Time: .... End Time: ....

► Today, I will talk with/communicate with Mr./ Ms./Dr. .... about:

EVENING REFLECTION

► The single most important thing I did today to get me closer to my goals was:

► The one thing that hurt my progress the most today was:

► I will overcome this obstacle tomorrow by:

"Achieving your goal is great. How you get there and with whom is more important."

—**DR. S.K. ELLIS,** *Investor & Entrepreneur*

MORNING PLANNING

► I choose to have joy today because:

► I am working towards my goal because:

My Plan A. is:

....

....

► The **first** thing I will do today to get me closer to achieving my Plan A. is:

Start Time: .... End Time: ....

► The **second** thing I will do today to get me closer to achieving my Plan A. is:

Start Time: .... End Time: ....

My next plan A is:

....

....

► The **first** thing I will do today to get me closer to achieving my next Plan A is:

Start Time: .... End Time: ....

► The **second** thing I will do today to get me closer to achieving my next Plan A is:

Start Time: .... End Time: ....

► Today, I will talk with/communicate with Mr./ Ms./Dr. .... about:

EVENING REFLECTION

► The single most important thing I did today to get me closer to my goals was:

► The one thing that hurt my progress the most today was:

► I will overcome this obstacle tomorrow by:

"Do not let the problems of others be a roadblock to your Success."

—**DR. S.K. ELLIS,** *Investor & Entrepreneur*

MORNING PLANNING

► I choose to have joy today because:

► I am working towards my goal because:

My Plan A. is:

....

....

► The **first** thing I will do today to get me closer to achieving my Plan A. is:

Start Time: .... End Time: ....

► The **second** thing I will do today to get me closer to achieving my Plan A. is:

Start Time: .... End Time: ....

My next plan A is:

....

....

► The **first** thing I will do today to get me closer to achieving my next Plan A is:

Start Time: .... End Time: ....

► The **second** thing I will do today to get me closer to achieving my next Plan A is:

Start Time: .... End Time: ....

► Today, I will talk with/communicate with Mr./ Ms./Dr. .... about:

EVENING REFLECTION

► The single most important thing I did today to get me closer to my goals was:

► The one thing that hurt my progress the most today was:

► I will overcome this obstacle tomorrow by:

"Once prayer becomes a habit, Success becomes a lifestyle."

—ANONYMOUS

MORNING PLANNING

► I choose to have joy today because:

► I am working towards my goal because:

My Plan A. is:

....

....

► The **first** thing I will do today to get me closer to achieving my Plan A. is:

Start Time: .... End Time: ....

► The **second** thing I will do today to get me closer to achieving my Plan A. is:

Start Time: .... End Time: ....

My next plan A is:

....

....

► The **first** thing I will do today to get me closer to achieving my next Plan A is:

Start Time: .... End Time: ....

► The **second** thing I will do today to get me closer to achieving my next Plan A is:

Start Time: .... End Time: ....

► Today, I will talk with/communicate with Mr./ Ms./Dr. .... about:

EVENING REFLECTION

► The single most important thing I did today to get me closer to my goals was:

► The one thing that hurt my progress the most today was:

► I will overcome this obstacle tomorrow by:

5-DAY ACCOUNTABILITY CHECK

During the past 5 days...

► I made time for my success by:

► I increased my knowledge about:

► I asked for advice/guidance from:

....

....

....

► Over the next 5 days I will talk with/communicate
with Mr./Ms./Dr. .... about:

"Good things come to those who wait, but only the things left by those who hustle."

—UNKNOWN

MORNING PLANNING

► I choose to have joy today because:

► I am working towards my goal because:

My Plan A. is:

....

....

► The **first** thing I will do today to get me closer to achieving my Plan A. is:

Start Time: .... End Time: ....

► The **second** thing I will do today to get me closer to achieving my Plan A. is:

Start Time: .... End Time: ....

My next plan A is:

....

....

► The **first** thing I will do today to get me closer to achieving my next Plan A is:

Start Time: .... End Time: ....

► The **second** thing I will do today to get me closer to achieving my next Plan A is:

Start Time: .... End Time: ....

► Today, I will talk with/communicate with Mr./ Ms./Dr. .... about:

EVENING REFLECTION

► The single most important thing I did today to get me closer to my goals was:

► The one thing that hurt my progress the most today was:

► I will overcome this obstacle tomorrow by:

"You can only have two things in life, reasons and results. Reasons do not count."

—ROBERT ANTHON, *Author*

MORNING PLANNING

► I choose to have joy today because:

► I am working towards my goal because:

My Plan A. is:

....

....

► The **first** thing I will do today to get me closer to achieving my Plan A. is:

Start Time: .... End Time: ....

► The **second** thing I will do today to get me closer to achieving my Plan A. is:

Start Time: .... End Time: ....

My next plan A is:

....

....

► The **first** thing I will do today to get me closer to achieving my next Plan A is:

Start Time: .... End Time: ....

► The **second** thing I will do today to get me closer to achieving my next Plan A is:

Start Time: .... End Time: ....

► Today, I will talk with/communicate with Mr./ Ms./Dr. .... about:

EVENING REFLECTION

► The single most important thing I did today to get me closer to my goals was:

► The one thing that hurt my progress the most today was:

► I will overcome this obstacle tomorrow by:

"The best way to predict the future is to invent it."

—**ALAN KAY,** *American Computer Scientist*

MORNING PLANNING

► I choose to have joy today because:

► I am working towards my goal because:

My Plan A. is:

....

....

► The **first** thing I will do today to get me closer to achieving my Plan A. is:

Start Time: .... End Time: ....

► The **second** thing I will do today to get me closer to achieving my Plan A. is:

Start Time: .... End Time: ....

My next plan A is:

....

....

► The **first** thing I will do today to get me closer to achieving my next Plan A is:

Start Time: .... End Time: ....

► The **second** thing I will do today to get me closer to achieving my next Plan A is:

Start Time: .... End Time: ....

► Today, I will talk with/communicate with Mr./ Ms./Dr. .... about:

EVENING REFLECTION

▶ The single most important thing I did today to get me closer to my goals was:

▶ The one thing that hurt my progress the most today was:

▶ I will overcome this obstacle tomorrow by:

The best revenge is massive Success.

—FRANK SINATRA, *Actor*

MORNING PLANNING

▶ I choose to have joy today because:

▶ I am working towards my goal because:

My Plan A. is:

....

....

► The **first** thing I will do today to get me closer to achieving my Plan A. is:

Start Time: .... End Time: ....

► The **second** thing I will do today to get me closer to achieving my Plan A. is:

Start Time: .... End Time: ....

My next plan A is:

....

....

► The **first** thing I will do today to get me closer to achieving my next Plan A is:

Start Time: .... End Time: ....

► The **second** thing I will do today to get me closer to achieving my next Plan A is:

Start Time: .... End Time: ....

► Today, I will talk with/communicate with Mr./Ms./Dr. .... about:

EVENING REFLECTION

► The single most important thing I did today to get me closer to my goals was:

► The one thing that hurt my progress the most today was:

► I will overcome this obstacle tomorrow by:

"There is nothing in this world that I cannot do something about even if it is nothing but to adjust myself to an unpleasant situation so that it does not destroy my spirit."

—NAPOLEAN HILL, *American Author*

MORNING PLANNING

► I choose to have joy today because:

► I am working towards my goal because:

My Plan A. is:

....

....

► The **first** thing I will do today to get me closer to achieving my Plan A. is:

Start Time: .... End Time: ....

► The **second** thing I will do today to get me closer to achieving my Plan A. is:

Start Time: .... End Time: ....

My next plan A is:

....

....

► The **first** thing I will do today to get me closer to achieving my next Plan A is:

Start Time: .... End Time: ....

► The **second** thing I will do today to get me closer to achieving my next Plan A is:

Start Time: .... End Time: ....

► Today, I will talk with/communicate with Mr./Ms./Dr. .... about:

EVENING REFLECTION

► The single most important thing I did today to get me closer to my goals was:

► The one thing that hurt my progress the most today was:

► I will overcome this obstacle tomorrow by:

5-DAY ACCOUNTABILITY CHECK

During the past 5 days...

► I made time for my success by:

► I increased my knowledge about:

► I asked for advice/guidance from:

....

....

....

► Over the next 5 days I will talk with/communicate with Mr./Ms./Dr. .... about:

"Hold yourself responsible for a higher standard than anybody expects of you. Never excuse yourself."

—HENRY WARD BEECHER, *American Minister*

MORNING PLANNING

► I choose to have joy today because:

► I am working towards my goal because:

My Plan A. is:

....

....

► The **first** thing I will do today to get me closer to achieving my Plan A. is:

Start Time: .... End Time: ....

► The **second** thing I will do today to get me closer to achieving my Plan A. is:

Start Time: .... End Time: ....

My next plan A is:

....

....

► The **first** thing I will do today to get me closer to achieving my next Plan A is:

Start Time: .... End Time: ....

► The **second** thing I will do today to get me closer to achieving my next Plan A is:

Start Time: .... End Time: ....

► Today, I will talk with/communicate with Mr./Ms./Dr. .... about:

EVENING REFLECTION

▶ The single most important thing I did today to get me closer to my goals was:

▶ The one thing that hurt my progress the most today was:

▶ I will overcome this obstacle tomorrow by:

"Do or do not. There is no try."

—YODA, *Jedi Master*

MORNING PLANNING

► I choose to have joy today because:

► I am working towards my goal because:

My Plan A. is:

....

....

► The **first** thing I will do today to get me closer to achieving my Plan A. is:

Start Time: .... End Time: ....

► The **second** thing I will do today to get me closer to achieving my Plan A. is:

Start Time: .... End Time: ....

My next plan A is:

....

....

► The **first** thing I will do today to get me closer to achieving my next Plan A is:

Start Time: .... End Time: ....

► The **second** thing I will do today to get me closer to achieving my next Plan A is:

Start Time: .... End Time: ....

► Today, I will talk with/communicate with Mr./ Ms./Dr. .... about:

EVENING REFLECTION

► The single most important thing I did today to get me closer to my goals was:

► The one thing that hurt my progress the most today was:

► I will overcome this obstacle tomorrow by:

"You can always go to the next level as long as you are willing to start at 1."

—**DR. S.K. ELLIS,** *Investor & Entrepreneur*

MORNING PLANNING

▶ I choose to have joy today because:

▶ I am working towards my goal because:

My Plan A. is:

....

....

▶ The **first** thing I will do today to get me closer to achieving my Plan A. is:

Start Time: .... End Time: ....

▶ The **second** thing I will do today to get me closer to achieving my Plan A. is:

Start Time: .... End Time: ....

My next plan A is:

....

....

► The **first** thing I will do today to get me closer to achieving my next Plan A is:

Start Time: .... End Time: ....

► The **second** thing I will do today to get me closer to achieving my next Plan A is:

Start Time: .... End Time: ....

► Today, I will talk with/communicate with Mr./Ms./Dr. .... about:

EVENING REFLECTION

▶ The single most important thing I did today to get me closer to my goals was:

```



```

▶ The one thing that hurt my progress the most today was:

```



```

▶ I will overcome this obstacle tomorrow by:

```



```

"Success is not a destination. Failure is not an event. Success is a process, failure is a choice."

—**DJ Benedict,** *Musical Artist*

MORNING PLANNING

► I choose to have joy today because:

► I am working towards my goal because:

My Plan A. is:

....

....

▶ The **first** thing I will do today to get me closer to achieving my Plan A. is:

Start Time: .... End Time: ....

▶ The **second** thing I will do today to get me closer to achieving my Plan A. is:

Start Time: .... End Time: ....

My next plan A is:

....

....

► The **first** thing I will do today to get me closer to achieving my next Plan A is:

Start Time: .... End Time: ....

► The **second** thing I will do today to get me closer to achieving my next Plan A is:

Start Time: .... End Time: ....

► Today, I will talk with/communicate with Mr./ Ms./Dr. .... about:

EVENING REFLECTION

► The single most important thing I did today to get me closer to my goals was:

► The one thing that hurt my progress the most today was:

► I will overcome this obstacle tomorrow by:

"Action cures fear."

—JASON LARITSEN, *Author*

MORNING PLANNING

▶ I choose to have joy today because:

▶ I am working towards my goal because:

My Plan A. is:

....

....

► The **first** thing I will do today to get me closer to achieving my Plan A. is:

Start Time: .... End Time: ....

► The **second** thing I will do today to get me closer to achieving my Plan A. is:

Start Time: .... End Time: ....

My next plan A is:

....

....

► The **first** thing I will do today to get me closer to achieving my next Plan A is:

Start Time: .... End Time: ....

► The **second** thing I will do today to get me closer to achieving my next Plan A is:

Start Time: .... End Time: ....

► Today, I will talk with/communicate with Mr./Ms./Dr. .... about:

EVENING REFLECTION

► The single most important thing I did today to get me closer to my goals was:

► The one thing that hurt my progress the most today was:

► I will overcome this obstacle tomorrow by:

5-DAY ACCOUNTABILITY CHECK

During the past 5 days...

► I made time for my success by:

► I increased my knowledge about:

► I asked for advice/guidance from:

....

....

....

► Over the next 5 days I will talk with/communicate with Mr./Ms./Dr. .... about:

3 BOOKS TO INSPIRE YOU

- ► *Think and Grow* Rich by Napolean Hill
- ► *SOAR* by T.D. Jakes
- ► *Grinding It Out: The Making of McDonalds* by Ray Kroc

"He holds Success in store for the upright; He is a shield for those whose walk is blameless."

—PROVERBS 2:7

MORNING PLANNING

► I choose to have joy today because:

► I am working towards my goal because:

My Plan A. is:

....

....

124

► The **first** thing I will do today to get me closer to achieving my Plan A. is:

Start Time: .... End Time: ....

► The **second** thing I will do today to get me closer to achieving my Plan A. is:

Start Time: .... End Time: ....

My next plan A is:

....

....

▶ The **first** thing I will do today to get me closer to achieving my next Plan A is:

Start Time: .... End Time: ....

▶ The **second** thing I will do today to get me closer to achieving my next Plan A is:

Start Time: .... End Time: ....

▶ Today, I will talk with/communicate with Mr./ Ms./Dr. .... about:

EVENING REFLECTION

▶ The single most important thing I did today to get me closer to my goals was:

▶ The one thing that hurt my progress the most today was:

▶ I will overcome this obstacle tomorrow by:

"Do not withhold good from those to whom it is due, when it is in your power to act. Do not say to your neighbor, "Come back tomorrow and I'll give it to you" —when you already have it with you."

—PROVERBS 3:27-29

MORNING PLANNING

► I choose to have joy today because:

► I am working towards my goal because:

My Plan A. is:

· ·

· ·

► The **first** thing I will do today to get me closer to achieving my Plan A. is:

Start Time: .... End Time: ....

► The **second** thing I will do today to get me closer to achieving my Plan A. is:

Start Time: .... End Time: ....

My next plan A is:

....

....

► The **first** thing I will do today to get me closer to achieving my next Plan A is:

Start Time: .... End Time: ....

► The **second** thing I will do today to get me closer to achieving my next Plan A is:

Start Time: .... End Time: ....

► Today, I will talk with/communicate with Mr./Ms./Dr. .... about:

EVENING REFLECTION

► The single most important thing I did today to get me closer to my goals was:

► The one thing that hurt my progress the most today was:

► I will overcome this obstacle tomorrow by:

"Whoever can be trusted with very little can also be trusted with much, and whoever is dishonest with very little will also be dishonest with much."

—LUKE **16:10**

MORNING PLANNING

► I choose to have joy today because:

► I am working towards my goal because:

My Plan A. is:

....

....

► The **first** thing I will do today to get me closer to achieving my Plan A. is:

Start Time: .... End Time: ....

► The **second** thing I will do today to get me closer to achieving my Plan A. is:

Start Time: .... End Time: ....

My next plan A is:

....

....

► The **first** thing I will do today to get me closer to achieving my next Plan A is:

Start Time: .... End Time: ....

► The **second** thing I will do today to get me closer to achieving my next Plan A is:

Start Time: .... End Time: ....

► Today, I will talk with/communicate with Mr./ Ms./Dr. .... about:

EVENING REFLECTION

▶ The single most important thing I did today to get me closer to my goals was:

▶ The one thing that hurt my progress the most today was:

▶ I will overcome this obstacle tomorrow by:

"But remember the LORD your God, for it is he who gives you the ability to produce wealth, and so confirms his covenant, which he swore to your ancestors, as it is today."

—DEUTERONOMY 8:18

MORNING PLANNING

► I choose to have joy today because:

► I am working towards my goal because:

My Plan A. is:

....

....

► The **first** thing I will do today to get me closer to achieving my Plan A. is:

Start Time: .... End Time: ....

► The **second** thing I will do today to get me closer to achieving my Plan A. is:

Start Time: .... End Time: ....

My next plan A is:

....

....

► The **first** thing I will do today to get me closer to achieving my next Plan A is:

Start Time: .... End Time: ....

► The **second** thing I will do today to get me closer to achieving my next Plan A is:

Start Time: .... End Time: ....

► Today, I will talk with/communicate with Mr./Ms./Dr. .... about:

EVENING REFLECTION

► The single most important thing I did today to get me closer to my goals was:

► The one thing that hurt my progress the most today was:

► I will overcome this obstacle tomorrow by:

"The generous soul will be made rich, and he who waters will also be watered himself."

—**Proverbs 13:4**

MORNING PLANNING

▶ I choose to have joy today because:

▶ I am working towards my goal because:

My Plan A. is:

....

....

► The **first** thing I will do today to get me closer to achieving my Plan A. is:

Start Time: .... End Time: ....

► The **second** thing I will do today to get me closer to achieving my Plan A. is:

Start Time: .... End Time: ....

My next plan A is:

....

....

► The **first** thing I will do today to get me closer to achieving my next Plan A is:

Start Time: .... End Time: ....

► The **second** thing I will do today to get me closer to achieving my next Plan A is:

Start Time: .... End Time: ....

► Today, I will talk with/communicate with Mr./Ms./Dr. .... about:

EVENING REFLECTION

▶ The single most important thing I did today to get me closer to my goals was:

▶ The one thing that hurt my progress the most today was:

▶ I will overcome this obstacle tomorrow by:

5-DAY ACCOUNTABILITY CHECK

During the past 5 days...

► I made time for my success by:

► I increased my knowledge about:

► I asked for advice/guidance from:

....

....

....

► Over the next 5 days I will talk with/communicate with Mr./Ms./Dr. .... about:

"Success is not the key to happiness. Happiness is the key to Success. If you love what you are doing, you will be Successful."

—HERMAN CAIN, *American Politician & Business Executive*

MORNING PLANNING

► I choose to have joy today because:

► I am working towards my goal because:

My Plan A. is:

....

....

► The **first** thing I will do today to get me closer to achieving my Plan A. is:

Start Time: .... End Time: ....

► The **second** thing I will do today to get me closer to achieving my Plan A. is:

Start Time: .... End Time: ....

My next plan A is:

....

....

► The **first** thing I will do today to get me closer to achieving my next Plan A is:

Start Time: .... End Time: ....

► The **second** thing I will do today to get me closer to achieving my next Plan A is:

Start Time: .... End Time: ....

► Today, I will talk with/communicate with Mr./Ms./Dr. .... about:

EVENING REFLECTION

▶ The single most important thing I did today to get me closer to my goals was:

▶ The one thing that hurt my progress the most today was:

▶ I will overcome this obstacle tomorrow by:

"Action is the fundamental key to Success."

—**PABLO PICASSO,** *Spanish Painter*

MORNING PLANNING

► I choose to have joy today because:

► I am working towards my goal because:

My Plan A. is:

....

....

► The **first** thing I will do today to get me closer to achieving my Plan A. is:

Start Time: .... End Time: ....

► The **second** thing I will do today to get me closer to achieving my Plan A. is:

Start Time: .... End Time: ....

My next plan A is:

....

....

► The **first** thing I will do today to get me closer to achieving my next Plan A is:

Start Time: .... End Time: ....

► The **second** thing I will do today to get me closer to achieving my next Plan A is:

Start Time: .... End Time: ....

► Today, I will talk with/communicate with Mr./ Ms./Dr. .... about:

EVENING REFLECTION

► The single most important thing I did today to get me closer to my goals was:

► The one thing that hurt my progress the most today was:

► I will overcome this obstacle tomorrow by:

"Success isn't about how much money you make. It's about the difference you make in people's lives."

—**MICHELLE OBAMA,**
Former First Lady of the United States of America

MORNING PLANNING

► I choose to have joy today because:

► I am working towards my goal because:

My Plan A. is:

....

....

► The **first** thing I will do today to get me closer to achieving my Plan A. is:

Start Time: .... End Time: ....

► The **second** thing I will do today to get me closer to achieving my Plan A. is:

Start Time: .... End Time: ....

My next plan A is:

....

....

► The **first** thing I will do today to get me closer to achieving my next Plan A is:

Start Time: .... End Time: ....

► The **second** thing I will do today to get me closer to achieving my next Plan A is:

Start Time: .... End Time: ....

► Today, I will talk with/communicate with Mr./ Ms./Dr. .... about:

EVENING REFLECTION

► The single most important thing I did today to get me closer to my goals was:

► The one thing that hurt my progress the most today was:

► I will overcome this obstacle tomorrow by:

"Success doesn't come to you; you've got to go to it."
—**MARVA COLLINS,** *American Educator*

MORNING PLANNING

▶ I choose to have joy today because:

▶ I am working towards my goal because:

My Plan A. is:

....

....

► The **first** thing I will do today to get me closer to achieving my Plan A. is:

Start Time: .... End Time: ....

► The **second** thing I will do today to get me closer to achieving my Plan A. is:

Start Time: .... End Time: ....

My next plan A is:

....

....

► The **first** thing I will do today to get me closer to achieving my next Plan A is:

Start Time: .... End Time: ....

► The **second** thing I will do today to get me closer to achieving my next Plan A is:

Start Time: .... End Time: ....

► Today, I will talk with/communicate with Mr./ Ms./Dr. .... about:

EVENING REFLECTION

► The single most important thing I did today to get me closer to my goals was:

► The one thing that hurt my progress the most today was:

► I will overcome this obstacle tomorrow by:

"I never dreamed about Success. I worked for it."

—ESTÉE LAUDER, *American Businesswoman*

MORNING PLANNING

► I choose to have joy today because:

► I am working towards my goal because:

My Plan A. is:

....

....

▶ The **first** thing I will do today to get me closer to achieving my Plan A. is:

Start Time: .... End Time: ....

▶ The **second** thing I will do today to get me closer to achieving my Plan A. is:

Start Time: .... End Time: ....

My next plan A is:

....

....

► The **first** thing I will do today to get me closer to achieving my next Plan A is:

Start Time: .... End Time: ....

► The **second** thing I will do today to get me closer to achieving my next Plan A is:

Start Time: .... End Time: ....

► Today, I will talk with/communicate with Mr./Ms./Dr. .... about:

EVENING REFLECTION

▶ The single most important thing I did today to get me closer to my goals was:

▶ The one thing that hurt my progress the most today was:

▶ I will overcome this obstacle tomorrow by:

165

5-DAY ACCOUNTABILITY CHECK

During the past 5 days...

► I made time for my success by:

► I increased my knowledge about:

► I asked for advice/guidance from:

....

....

....

► Over the next 5 days I will talk with/communicate with Mr./Ms./Dr. .... about:

"Success means having the courage, the determination, and the will to become the person you believe you were meant to be."

—**GEORGE SHEEHAN,** *Physician & Author*

MORNING PLANNING

► I choose to have joy today because:

► I am working towards my goal because:

My Plan A. is:

....

....

► The **first** thing I will do today to get me closer to achieving my Plan A. is:

Start Time: .... End Time: ....

► The **second** thing I will do today to get me closer to achieving my Plan A. is:

Start Time: .... End Time: ....

My next plan A is:

....

....

► The **first** thing I will do today to get me closer to achieving my next Plan A is:

Start Time: ....   End Time: ....

► The **second** thing I will do today to get me closer to achieving my next Plan A is:

Start Time: ....   End Time: ....

► Today, I will talk with/communicate with Mr./ Ms./Dr. .... about:

EVENING REFLECTION

► The single most important thing I did today to get me closer to my goals was:

► The one thing that hurt my progress the most today was:

► I will overcome this obstacle tomorrow by:

"If you really want to do something, you will find a way. If you do not, you'll find an excuse."

—JIM ROHN, *American Entrepreneur*

MORNING PLANNING

▶ I choose to have joy today because:

▶ I am working towards my goal because:

My Plan A. is:

....

....

▶ The **first** thing I will do today to get me closer to achieving my Plan A. is:

Start Time: .... End Time: ....

▶ The **second** thing I will do today to get me closer to achieving my Plan A. is:

Start Time: .... End Time: ....

My next plan A is:

....

....

► The **first** thing I will do today to get me closer to achieving my next Plan A is:

Start Time: .... End Time: ....

► The **second** thing I will do today to get me closer to achieving my next Plan A is:

Start Time: .... End Time: ....

► Today, I will talk with/communicate with Mr./Ms./Dr. .... about:

EVENING REFLECTION

▶ The single most important thing I did today to get me closer to my goals was:

▶ The one thing that hurt my progress the most today was:

▶ I will overcome this obstacle tomorrow by:

"You always pass failure on the way to Success."

—**MICKEY ROONEY,** *American Actor*

MORNING PLANNING

► I choose to have joy today because:

► I am working towards my goal because:

My Plan A. is:

....

....

► The **first** thing I will do today to get me closer to achieving my Plan A. is:

Start Time: .... End Time: ....

► The **second** thing I will do today to get me closer to achieving my Plan A. is:

Start Time: .... End Time: ....

My next plan A is:

....

....

► The **first** thing I will do today to get me closer to achieving my next Plan A is:

Start Time: .... End Time: ....

► The **second** thing I will do today to get me closer to achieving my next Plan A is:

Start Time: .... End Time: ....

► Today, I will talk with/communicate with Mr./ Ms./Dr. .... about:

EVENING REFLECTION

► The single most important thing I did today to get me closer to my goals was:

► The one thing that hurt my progress the most today was:

► I will overcome this obstacle tomorrow by:

"Success comes in cans; failure in can nots."

—WILFRED PETERSON, *American Author*

MORNING PLANNING

► I choose to have joy today because:

► I am working towards my goal because:

My Plan A. is:

....

....

► The **first** thing I will do today to get me closer to achieving my Plan A. is:

Start Time: ....   End Time: ....

► The **second** thing I will do today to get me closer to achieving my Plan A. is:

Start Time: ....   End Time: ....

My next plan A is:

....

....

► The **first** thing I will do today to get me closer to achieving my next Plan A is:

Start Time: .... End Time: ....

► The **second** thing I will do today to get me closer to achieving my next Plan A is:

Start Time: .... End Time: ....

► Today, I will talk with/communicate with Mr./Ms./Dr. .... about:

EVENING REFLECTION

► The single most important thing I did today to get me closer to my goals was:

► The one thing that hurt my progress the most today was:

► I will overcome this obstacle tomorrow by:

"The dictionary is the only place where Success comes before work."

—**MARK TWAIN,** *American Writer*

MORNING PLANNING

► I choose to have joy today because:

► I am working towards my goal because:

My Plan A. is:

....

....

► The **first** thing I will do today to get me closer to achieving my Plan A. is:

Start Time: .... End Time: ....

► The **second** thing I will do today to get me closer to achieving my Plan A. is:

Start Time: .... End Time: ....

My next plan A is:

....

....

► The **first** thing I will do today to get me closer to achieving my next Plan A is:

Start Time: .... End Time: ....

► The **second** thing I will do today to get me closer to achieving my next Plan A is:

Start Time: .... End Time: ....

► Today, I will talk with/communicate with Mr./Ms./Dr. .... about:

EVENING REFLECTION

▶ The single most important thing I did today to get me closer to my goals was:

▶ The one thing that hurt my progress the most today was:

▶ I will overcome this obstacle tomorrow by:

5-DAY ACCOUNTABILITY CHECK

During the past 5 days...

► I made time for my success by:

► I increased my knowledge about:

► I asked for advice/guidance from:

....

....

....

► Over the next 5 days I will talk with/communicate with Mr./Ms./Dr. .... about:

"The soul of a lazy man desires, and has nothing; but the soul of the diligent shall be made rich."

—PROVERBS 13:4

MORNING PLANNING

► I choose to have joy today because:

► I am working towards my goal because:

My Plan A. is:

....

....

► The **first** thing I will do today to get me closer to achieving my Plan A. is:

Start Time: .... End Time: ....

► The **second** thing I will do today to get me closer to achieving my Plan A. is:

Start Time: .... End Time: ....

My next plan A is:

....

....

► The **first** thing I will do today to get me closer to achieving my next Plan A is:

Start Time: .... End Time: ....

► The **second** thing I will do today to get me closer to achieving my next Plan A is:

Start Time: .... End Time: ....

► Today, I will talk with/communicate with Mr./ Ms./Dr. .... about:

EVENING REFLECTION

► The single most important thing I did today to get me closer to my goals was:

► The one thing that hurt my progress the most today was:

► I will overcome this obstacle tomorrow by:

"Beloved, I pray that you may prosper in all things and be in health, just as your soul prospers."

—3 John 2

MORNING PLANNING

► I choose to have joy today because:

► I am working towards my goal because:

My Plan A. is:

....

....

► The **first** thing I will do today to get me closer to achieving my Plan A. is:

Start Time: .... End Time: ....

► The **second** thing I will do today to get me closer to achieving my Plan A. is:

Start Time: .... End Time: ....

My next plan A is:

....

....

► The **first** thing I will do today to get me closer to achieving my next Plan A is:

Start Time: .... End Time: ....

► The **second** thing I will do today to get me closer to achieving my next Plan A is:

Start Time: .... End Time: ....

► Today, I will talk with/communicate with Mr./Ms./Dr. .... about:

EVENING REFLECTION

▶ The single most important thing I did today to get me closer to my goals was:

▶ The one thing that hurt my progress the most today was:

▶ I will overcome this obstacle tomorrow by:

"The best among you are those who have the best manners and best character."

—Sᴀʜɪʜ Bᴜᴋʜᴀʀɪ **6029**

MORNING PLANNING

► I choose to have joy today because:

► I am working towards my goal because:

My Plan A. is:

....

....

► The **first** thing I will do today to get me closer to achieving my Plan A. is:

Start Time: .... End Time: ....

► The **second** thing I will do today to get me closer to achieving my Plan A. is:

Start Time: .... End Time: ....

My next plan A is:

....

....

► The **first** thing I will do today to get me closer to achieving my next Plan A is:

Start Time: .... End Time: ....

► The **second** thing I will do today to get me closer to achieving my next Plan A is:

Start Time: .... End Time: ....

► Today, I will talk with/communicate with Mr./Ms./Dr. .... about:

EVENING REFLECTION

▶ The single most important thing I did today to get me closer to my goals was:

▶ The one thing that hurt my progress the most today was:

▶ I will overcome this obstacle tomorrow by:

"The richest of the rich is the one who is not a prisoner to greed."

—ALI IBN ABI TALIB (R.A.)

MORNING PLANNING

▶ I choose to have joy today because:

▶ I am working towards my goal because:

My Plan A. is:

....

....

► The **first** thing I will do today to get me closer to achieving my Plan A. is:

Start Time: .... End Time: ....

► The **second** thing I will do today to get me closer to achieving my Plan A. is:

Start Time: .... End Time: ....

My next plan A is:

....

....

► The **first** thing I will do today to get me closer to achieving my next Plan A is:

Start Time: .... End Time: ....

► The **second** thing I will do today to get me closer to achieving my next Plan A is:

Start Time: .... End Time: ....

► Today, I will talk with/communicate with Mr./ Ms./Dr. .... about:

EVENING REFLECTION

► The single most important thing I did today to get me closer to my goals was:

► The one thing that hurt my progress the most today was:

► I will overcome this obstacle tomorrow by:

"Be like a diamond, precious and rare, not like a stone, found everywhere."

—ANONYMOUS

MORNING PLANNING

► I choose to have joy today because:

► I am working towards my goal because:

My Plan A. is:

....

....

▶ The **first** thing I will do today to get me closer to achieving my Plan A. is:

Start Time: .... End Time: ....

▶ The **second** thing I will do today to get me closer to achieving my Plan A. is:

Start Time: .... End Time: ....

My next plan A is:

....

....

► The **first** thing I will do today to get me closer to achieving my next Plan A is:

Start Time: .... End Time: ....

► The **second** thing I will do today to get me closer to achieving my next Plan A is:

Start Time: .... End Time: ....

► Today, I will talk with/communicate with Mr./Ms./Dr. .... about:

EVENING REFLECTION

► The single most important thing I did today to get me closer to my goals was:

► The one thing that hurt my progress the most today was:

► I will overcome this obstacle tomorrow by:

5-DAY ACCOUNTABILITY CHECK

During the past 5 days...

► I made time for my success by:

► I increased my knowledge about:

► I asked for advice/guidance from:

....

....

....

► Over the next 5 days I will talk with/communicate with Mr./Ms./Dr. .... about:

3 BOOKS TO EMPOWER YOU

► *How to Win Friends and Influence People* by Dale Carnegie

► *Raving* Fans by Kenneth H. Blanchard & Sheldon Bowles

► *Atomic Habits* by James Clear

► Bonus Recommendation: *Introduction to Personal Branding* by Mel Carlson

"Do not let what you can not do stop you from doing what you can do."

–JOHN WOODEN, *American Basketball Player*

MORNING PLANNING

► I choose to have joy today because:

► I am working towards my goal because:

My Plan A. is:

....

....

► The **first** thing I will do today to get me closer to achieving my Plan A. is:

Start Time: .... End Time: ....

► The **second** thing I will do today to get me closer to achieving my Plan A. is:

Start Time: .... End Time: ....

My next plan A is:

....

....

► The **first** thing I will do today to get me closer to achieving my next Plan A is:

Start Time: .... End Time: ....

► The **second** thing I will do today to get me closer to achieving my next Plan A is:

Start Time: .... End Time: ....

► Today, I will talk with/communicate with Mr./Ms./Dr. .... about:

EVENING REFLECTION

► The single most important thing I did today to get me closer to my goals was:

► The one thing that hurt my progress the most today was:

► I will overcome this obstacle tomorrow by:

"It's not what happens to you, but how you react to it that matters."

—**EPICTETUS**, *Greek Philosopher*

MORNING PLANNING

► I choose to have joy today because:

► I am working towards my goal because:

My Plan A. is:

....

....

▶ The **first** thing I will do today to get me closer to achieving my Plan A. is:

Start Time: .... End Time: ....

▶ The **second** thing I will do today to get me closer to achieving my Plan A. is:

Start Time: .... End Time: ....

My next plan A is:

....

....

► The **first** thing I will do today to get me closer to achieving my next Plan A is:

Start Time: .... End Time: ....

► The **second** thing I will do today to get me closer to achieving my next Plan A is:

Start Time: .... End Time: ....

► Today, I will talk with/communicate with Mr./ Ms./Dr. .... about:

EVENING REFLECTION

▶ The single most important thing I did today to get me closer to my goals was:

▶ The one thing that hurt my progress the most today was:

▶ I will overcome this obstacle tomorrow by:

"Only surround yourself with people who will lift you higher."

—OPRAH WINFREY, *American Executive & Entrepreneur*

MORNING PLANNING

▶ I choose to have joy today because:

▶ I am working towards my goal because:

My Plan A. is:

....

....

► The **first** thing I will do today to get me closer to achieving my Plan A. is:

Start Time: .... End Time: ....

► The **second** thing I will do today to get me closer to achieving my Plan A. is:

Start Time: .... End Time: ....

My next plan A is:

....

....

► The **first** thing I will do today to get me closer to achieving my next Plan A is:

Start Time: .... End Time: ....

► The **second** thing I will do today to get me closer to achieving my next Plan A is:

Start Time: .... End Time: ....

► Today, I will talk with/communicate with Mr./Ms./Dr. .... about:

EVENING REFLECTION

► The single most important thing I did today to get me closer to my goals was:

► The one thing that hurt my progress the most today was:

► I will overcome this obstacle tomorrow by:

"You can steer yourself any direction you choose."

—**DR. SEUSS,** *American Author*

MORNING PLANNING

▶ I choose to have joy today because:

▶ I am working towards my goal because:

My Plan A. is:

....

....

▶ The **first** thing I will do today to get me closer to achieving my Plan A. is:

Start Time: .... End Time: ....

▶ The **second** thing I will do today to get me closer to achieving my Plan A. is:

Start Time: .... End Time: ....

My next plan A is:

....

....

► The **first** thing I will do today to get me closer to achieving my next Plan A is:

Start Time: .... End Time: ....

► The **second** thing I will do today to get me closer to achieving my next Plan A is:

Start Time: .... End Time: ....

► Today, I will talk with/communicate with Mr./Ms./Dr. .... about:

EVENING REFLECTION

► The single most important thing I did today to get me closer to my goals was:

► The one thing that hurt my progress the most today was:

► I will overcome this obstacle tomorrow by:

"Winning doesn't always mean being first. Winning means you are doing better than you've done before."

—**BONNIE BLAIR,** *American Speed Skater*

MORNING PLANNING

▶ I choose to have joy today because:

▶ I am working towards my goal because:

My Plan A. is:

....

....

► The **first** thing I will do today to get me closer to achieving my Plan A. is:

Start Time: .... End Time: ....

► The **second** thing I will do today to get me closer to achieving my Plan A. is:

Start Time: .... End Time: ....

My next plan A is:

....

....

► The **first** thing I will do today to get me closer to achieving my next Plan A is:

Start Time: .... End Time: ....

► The **second** thing I will do today to get me closer to achieving my next Plan A is:

Start Time: .... End Time: ....

► Today, I will talk with/communicate with Mr./ Ms./Dr. .... about:

EVENING REFLECTION

► The single most important thing I did today to get me closer to my goals was:

► The one thing that hurt my progress the most today was:

► I will overcome this obstacle tomorrow by:

5-DAY ACCOUNTABILITY CHECK

During the past 5 days...

► I made time for my success by:

► I increased my knowledge about:

► I asked for advice/guidance from:

....

....

....

► Over the next 5 days I will talk with/communicate
with Mr./Ms./Dr. .... about:

"Nothing is particularly hard if you break it down into small jobs."

—HENRY FORD, *American industrialist &*
Business Magnate

MORNING PLANNING

► I choose to have joy today because:

► I am working towards my goal because:

My Plan A. is:

....

....

▶ The **first** thing I will do today to get me closer to achieving my Plan A. is:

Start Time: .... End Time: ....

▶ The **second** thing I will do today to get me closer to achieving my Plan A. is:

Start Time: .... End Time: ....

My next plan A is:

....

....

► The **first** thing I will do today to get me closer to achieving my next Plan A is:

Start Time: .... End Time: ....

► The **second** thing I will do today to get me closer to achieving my next Plan A is:

Start Time: .... End Time: ....

► Today, I will talk with/communicate with Mr./ Ms./Dr. .... about:

EVENING REFLECTION

▶ The single most important thing I did today to get me closer to my goals was:

▶ The one thing that hurt my progress the most today was:

▶ I will overcome this obstacle tomorrow by:

"Success is a state of mind. If you want Success, start thinking of yourself as a Success."

—JOYCE BROTHERS, *American Psychologist*

MORNING PLANNING

► I choose to have joy today because:

► I am working towards my goal because:

My Plan A. is:

....

....

► The **first** thing I will do today to get me closer to achieving my Plan A. is:

Start Time: .... End Time: ....

► The **second** thing I will do today to get me closer to achieving my Plan A. is:

Start Time: .... End Time: ....

My next plan A is:

....

....

► The **first** thing I will do today to get me closer to achieving my next Plan A is:

Start Time: .... End Time: ....

► The **second** thing I will do today to get me closer to achieving my next Plan A is:

Start Time: .... End Time: ....

► Today, I will talk with/communicate with Mr./ Ms./Dr. .... about:

EVENING REFLECTION

► The single most important thing I did today to get me closer to my goals was:

► The one thing that hurt my progress the most today was:

► I will overcome this obstacle tomorrow by:

"If I cannot do great things, I can do small things in a great way."

—**Dr. Martin Luther King, Jr.,**
American Minister & Civil Rights Activist

MORNING PLANNING

► I choose to have joy today because:

► I am working towards my goal because:

My Plan A. is:

....

....

▶ The **first** thing I will do today to get me closer to achieving my Plan A. is:

Start Time: .... End Time: ....

▶ The **second** thing I will do today to get me closer to achieving my Plan A. is:

Start Time: .... End Time: ....

My next plan A is:

....

....

► The **first** thing I will do today to get me closer to achieving my next Plan A is:

Start Time: .... End Time: ....

► The **second** thing I will do today to get me closer to achieving my next Plan A is:

Start Time: .... End Time: ....

► Today, I will talk with/communicate with Mr./Ms./Dr. .... about:

EVENING REFLECTION

► The single most important thing I did today to get me closer to my goals was:

► The one thing that hurt my progress the most today was:

► I will overcome this obstacle tomorrow by:

"In order to attain the impossible, one must attempt the absurd."

—**MIGUEL DE CERVANTES,** *Spanish Writer*

MORNING PLANNING

► I choose to have joy today because:

► I am working towards my goal because:

My Plan A. is:

....

....

► The **first** thing I will do today to get me closer to achieving my Plan A. is:

Start Time: .... End Time: ....

► The **second** thing I will do today to get me closer to achieving my Plan A. is:

Start Time: .... End Time: ....

My next plan A is:

....

....

► The **first** thing I will do today to get me closer to achieving my next Plan A is:

Start Time: .... End Time: ....

► The **second** thing I will do today to get me closer to achieving my next Plan A is:

Start Time: .... End Time: ....

► Today, I will talk with/communicate with Mr./Ms./Dr. .... about:

EVENING REFLECTION

► The single most important thing I did today to get me closer to my goals was:

► The one thing that hurt my progress the most today was:

► I will overcome this obstacle tomorrow by:

"All you need in this life is ignorance and confidence, and then Success is sure."

—**MARK TWAIN,** *American Writer*

MORNING PLANNING

► I choose to have joy today because:

► I am working towards my goal because:

My Plan A. is:

....

....

► The **first** thing I will do today to get me closer to achieving my Plan A. is:

Start Time: .... End Time: ....

► The **second** thing I will do today to get me closer to achieving my Plan A. is:

Start Time: .... End Time: ....

My next plan A is:

....

....

► The **first** thing I will do today to get me closer to achieving my next Plan A is:

Start Time: .... End Time: ....

► The **second** thing I will do today to get me closer to achieving my next Plan A is:

Start Time: .... End Time: ....

► Today, I will talk with/communicate with Mr./Ms./Dr. .... about:

EVENING REFLECTION

▶ The single most important thing I did today to get me closer to my goals was:

▶ The one thing that hurt my progress the most today was:

▶ I will overcome this obstacle tomorrow by:

5-DAY ACCOUNTABILITY CHECK

During the past 5 days...

► I made time for my success by:

► I increased my knowledge about:

► I asked for advice/guidance from:

....

....

....

► Over the next 5 days I will talk with/communicate with Mr./Ms./Dr. .... about:

"If you have not critics, it is likely you will have no Success."

—**MALCOLM X,** *American Minister &*
Human Rights Activist

MORNING PLANNING

► I choose to have joy today because:

► I am working towards my goal because:

My Plan A. is:

....

....

► The **first** thing I will do today to get me closer to achieving my Plan A. is:

Start Time: .... End Time: ....

► The **second** thing I will do today to get me closer to achieving my Plan A. is:

Start Time: .... End Time: ....

My next plan A is:

....

....

► The **first** thing I will do today to get me closer to achieving my next Plan A is:

Start Time: .... End Time: ....

► The **second** thing I will do today to get me closer to achieving my next Plan A is:

Start Time: .... End Time: ....

► Today, I will talk with/communicate with Mr./ Ms./Dr. .... about:

EVENING REFLECTION

► The single most important thing I did today to get me closer to my goals was:

► The one thing that hurt my progress the most today was:

► I will overcome this obstacle tomorrow by:

"Success is nothing more than a few simple disciplines, practiced every day."

—**JIM ROHN,** *American Entrepreneur & Author*

MORNING PLANNING

► I choose to have joy today because:

► I am working towards my goal because:

My Plan A. is:

....

....

► The **first** thing I will do today to get me closer to achieving my Plan A. is:

Start Time: .... End Time: ....

► The **second** thing I will do today to get me closer to achieving my Plan A. is:

Start Time: .... End Time: ....

My next plan A is:

....

....

► The **first** thing I will do today to get me closer to achieving my next Plan A is:

Start Time: .... End Time: ....

► The **second** thing I will do today to get me closer to achieving my next Plan A is:

Start Time: .... End Time: ....

► Today, I will talk with/communicate with Mr./ Ms./Dr. .... about:

EVENING REFLECTION

▶ The single most important thing I did today to get me closer to my goals was:

$$\text{(blank box)}$$

▶ The one thing that hurt my progress the most today was:

$$\text{(blank box)}$$

▶ I will overcome this obstacle tomorrow by:

$$\text{(blank box)}$$

"Make each day your masterpiece."

—JOHN WOODEN, *American Basketball Player*

MORNING PLANNING

▶ I choose to have joy today because:

▶ I am working towards my goal because:

My Plan A. is:

....

....

► The **first** thing I will do today to get me closer to achieving my Plan A. is:

Start Time: .... End Time: ....

► The **second** thing I will do today to get me closer to achieving my Plan A. is:

Start Time: .... End Time: ....

My next plan A is:

....

....

► The **first** thing I will do today to get me closer to achieving my next Plan A is:

Start Time: .... End Time: ....

► The **second** thing I will do today to get me closer to achieving my next Plan A is:

Start Time: .... End Time: ....

► Today, I will talk with/communicate with Mr./Ms./Dr. .... about:

EVENING REFLECTION

► The single most important thing I did today to get me closer to my goals was:

► The one thing that hurt my progress the most today was:

► I will overcome this obstacle tomorrow by:

"There's no elevator to Success. You have to take the stairs."

—UNKNOWN

MORNING PLANNING

► I choose to have joy today because:

► I am working towards my goal because:

My Plan A. is:

....

....

► The **first** thing I will do today to get me closer to achieving my Plan A. is:

Start Time: .... End Time: ....

► The **second** thing I will do today to get me closer to achieving my Plan A. is:

Start Time: .... End Time: ....

My next plan A is:

....

....

► The **first** thing I will do today to get me closer to achieving my next Plan A is:

Start Time: .... End Time: ....

► The **second** thing I will do today to get me closer to achieving my next Plan A is:

Start Time: .... End Time: ....

► Today, I will talk with/communicate with Mr./ Ms./Dr. .... about:

EVENING REFLECTION

▶ The single most important thing I did today to get me closer to my goals was:

▶ The one thing that hurt my progress the most today was:

▶ I will overcome this obstacle tomorrow by:

"He who has pity on the poor lends to the Lord, and He will pay back what he has given."

—PROVERBS 13:4

MORNING PLANNING

► I choose to have joy today because:

► I am working towards my goal because:

My Plan A. is:

....

....

► The **first** thing I will do today to get me closer to achieving my Plan A. is:

Start Time: .... End Time: ....

► The **second** thing I will do today to get me closer to achieving my Plan A. is:

Start Time: .... End Time: ....

My next plan A is:

....

....

► The **first** thing I will do today to get me closer to achieving my next Plan A is:

Start Time: .... End Time: ....

► The **second** thing I will do today to get me closer to achieving my next Plan A is:

Start Time: .... End Time: ....

► Today, I will talk with/communicate with Mr./Ms./Dr. .... about:

EVENING REFLECTION

► The single most important thing I did today to get me closer to my goals was:

► The one thing that hurt my progress the most today was:

► I will overcome this obstacle tomorrow by:

5-DAY ACCOUNTABILITY CHECK

During the past 5 days...

► I made time for my success by:

► I increased my knowledge about:

► I asked for advice/guidance from:

....

....

....

► Over the next 5 days I will talk with/communicate with Mr./Ms./Dr. .... about:

"If they obey and serve Him, they shall spend their days in prosperity, and their years in pleasures."

–JOB 36:11

MORNING PLANNING

▶ I choose to have joy today because:

▶ I am working towards my goal because:

My Plan A. is:

....

....

► The **first** thing I will do today to get me closer to achieving my Plan A. is:

Start Time: .... End Time: ....

► The **second** thing I will do today to get me closer to achieving my Plan A. is:

Start Time: .... End Time: ....

My next plan A is:

....

....

► The **first** thing I will do today to get me closer to achieving my next Plan A is:

Start Time: .... End Time: ....

► The **second** thing I will do today to get me closer to achieving my next Plan A is:

Start Time: .... End Time: ....

► Today, I will talk with/communicate with Mr./ Ms./Dr. .... about:

EVENING REFLECTION

► The single most important thing I did today to get me closer to my goals was:

► The one thing that hurt my progress the most today was:

► I will overcome this obstacle tomorrow by:

"He sought God in the days of Zechariah, who had understanding in the visions of God; and as long as he sought the Lord, God made him prosper."

—2 CHRONICLES 26:5

MORNING PLANNING

▶ I choose to have joy today because:

▶ I am working towards my goal because:

My Plan A. is:

....

....

► The **first** thing I will do today to get me closer to achieving my Plan A. is:

Start Time: .... End Time: ....

► The **second** thing I will do today to get me closer to achieving my Plan A. is:

Start Time: .... End Time: ....

My next plan A is:

....

....

▶ The **first** thing I will do today to get me closer to achieving my next Plan A is:

Start Time: .... End Time: ....

▶ The **second** thing I will do today to get me closer to achieving my next Plan A is:

Start Time: .... End Time: ....

▶ Today, I will talk with/communicate with Mr./ Ms./Dr. .... about:

EVENING REFLECTION

► The single most important thing I did today to get me closer to my goals was:

► The one thing that hurt my progress the most today was:

► I will overcome this obstacle tomorrow by:

"Luck is a return of and a return on investment. Invest more, get luckier."

—**Dr. S.K. Ellis,** *Investor & Entrepreneur*

MORNING PLANNING

▶ I choose to have joy today because:

▶ I am working towards my goal because:

My Plan A. is:

....

....

► The **first** thing I will do today to get me closer to achieving my Plan A. is:

Start Time: .... End Time: ....

► The **second** thing I will do today to get me closer to achieving my Plan A. is:

Start Time: .... End Time: ....

My next plan A is:

....

....

► The **first** thing I will do today to get me closer to achieving my next Plan A is:

Start Time: .... End Time: ....

► The **second** thing I will do today to get me closer to achieving my next Plan A is:

Start Time: .... End Time: ....

► Today, I will talk with/communicate with Mr./ Ms./Dr. .... about:

EVENING REFLECTION

► The single most important thing I did today to get me closer to my goals was:

► The one thing that hurt my progress the most today was:

► I will overcome this obstacle tomorrow by:

"There is little Success where there is little laughter."

—ANDREW CARNEGIE,
American Industrialist & Businessman

MORNING PLANNING

▶   I choose to have joy today because:

▶   I am working towards my goal because:

My Plan A. is:

....

....

► The **first** thing I will do today to get me closer to achieving my Plan A. is:

Start Time: .... End Time: ....

► The **second** thing I will do today to get me closer to achieving my Plan A. is:

Start Time: .... End Time: ....

My next plan A is:

....

....

► The **first** thing I will do today to get me closer to achieving my next Plan A is:

Start Time: .... End Time: ....

► The **second** thing I will do today to get me closer to achieving my next Plan A is:

Start Time: .... End Time: ....

► Today, I will talk with/communicate with Mr./ Ms./Dr. .... about:

EVENING REFLECTION

► The single most important thing I did today to get me closer to my goals was:

► The one thing that hurt my progress the most today was:

► I will overcome this obstacle tomorrow by:

"The ladder of Success is best climbed by stepping on the rungs of opportunity."

—**AYN RAND,** *Writer*

MORNING PLANNING

▶ I choose to have joy today because:

▶ I am working towards my goal because:

My Plan A. is:

....

....

► The **first** thing I will do today to get me closer to achieving my Plan A. is:

Start Time: .... End Time: ....

► The **second** thing I will do today to get me closer to achieving my Plan A. is:

Start Time: .... End Time: ....

My next plan A is:

....

....

► The **first** thing I will do today to get me closer to achieving my next Plan A is:

Start Time: .... End Time: ....

► The **second** thing I will do today to get me closer to achieving my next Plan A is:

Start Time: .... End Time: ....

► Today, I will talk with/communicate with Mr./Ms./Dr. .... about:

EVENING REFLECTION

▶ The single most important thing I did today to get me closer to my goals was:

▶ The one thing that hurt my progress the most today was:

▶ I will overcome this obstacle tomorrow by:

5-DAY ACCOUNTABILITY CHECK

During the past 5 days...

► I made time for my success by:

► I increased my knowledge about:

► I asked for advice/guidance from:

....

....

....

► Over the next 5 days I will talk with/communicate with Mr./Ms./Dr. .... about:

"Do not wait for the Spirit to move you. Move first, and make the spirit catch up.

—**Dr. S.K. Ellis**, *Investor & Entrepreneur*

MORNING PLANNING

► I choose to have joy today because:

► I am working towards my goal because:

My Plan A. is:

....

....

► The **first** thing I will do today to get me closer to achieving my Plan A. is:

Start Time: .... End Time: ....

► The **second** thing I will do today to get me closer to achieving my Plan A. is:

Start Time: .... End Time: ....

My next plan A is:

....

....

► The **first** thing I will do today to get me closer to achieving my next Plan A is:

Start Time: .... End Time: ....

► The **second** thing I will do today to get me closer to achieving my next Plan A is:

Start Time: .... End Time: ....

► Today, I will talk with/communicate with Mr./ Ms./Dr. .... about:

EVENING REFLECTION

▶ The single most important thing I did today to get me closer to my goals was:

▶ The one thing that hurt my progress the most today was:

▶ I will overcome this obstacle tomorrow by:

"Do not be anxious about anything, but in every situation, by prayer and petition, with thanksgiving, present your requests to God."

—PHILLIPIANS 4:6

MORNING PLANNING

► I choose to have joy today because:

► I am working towards my goal because:

My Plan A. is:

....

....

► The **first** thing I will do today to get me closer to achieving my Plan A. is:

Start Time: .... End Time: ....

► The **second** thing I will do today to get me closer to achieving my Plan A. is:

Start Time: .... End Time: ....

My next plan A is:

....

....

► The **first** thing I will do today to get me closer to achieving my next Plan A is:

Start Time: .... End Time: ....

► The **second** thing I will do today to get me closer to achieving my next Plan A is:

Start Time: .... End Time: ....

► Today, I will talk with/communicate with Mr./ Ms./Dr. .... about:

EVENING REFLECTION

► The single most important thing I did today to get me closer to my goals was:

► The one thing that hurt my progress the most today was:

► I will overcome this obstacle tomorrow by:

"Upgrade your dream to match your faith; do not downgrade your faith to match your dream."

—**Dr. S.K. Ellis,** *Investor & Entrepreneur*

MORNING PLANNING

▶ I choose to have joy today because:

▶ I am working towards my goal because:

My Plan A. is:

....

....

► The **first** thing I will do today to get me closer to achieving my Plan A. is:

Start Time: .... End Time: ....

► The **second** thing I will do today to get me closer to achieving my Plan A. is:

Start Time: .... End Time: ....

My next plan A is:

....

....

► The **first** thing I will do today to get me closer to achieving my next Plan A is:

Start Time: .... End Time: ....

► The **second** thing I will do today to get me closer to achieving my next Plan A is:

Start Time: .... End Time: ....

► Today, I will talk with/communicate with Mr./ Ms./Dr. .... about:

EVENING REFLECTION

► The single most important thing I did today to get me closer to my goals was:

► The one thing that hurt my progress the most today was:

► I will overcome this obstacle tomorrow by:

"Then you will prosper, if you take care to fulfill the statutes and judgments with which the Lord charged Moses concerning Israel. Be strong and of good courage; do not fear nor be dismayed."

—1 Chronicles 22:13

MORNING PLANNING

▶ I choose to have joy today because:

▶ I am working towards my goal because:

My Plan A. is:

....

....

► The **first** thing I will do today to get me closer to achieving my Plan A. is:

Start Time: .... End Time: ....

► The **second** thing I will do today to get me closer to achieving my Plan A. is:

Start Time: .... End Time: ....

My next plan A is:

....

....

► The **first** thing I will do today to get me closer to achieving my next Plan A is:

Start Time: .... End Time: ....

► The **second** thing I will do today to get me closer to achieving my next Plan A is:

Start Time: .... End Time: ....

► Today, I will talk with/communicate with Mr./ Ms./Dr. .... about:

EVENING REFLECTION

► The single most important thing I did today to get me closer to my goals was:

► The one thing that hurt my progress the most today was:

► I will overcome this obstacle tomorrow by:

"Wisdom is the principal thing; therefore get wisdom: and with all thy getting get understanding."

—PROVERBS 4:7

MORNING PLANNING

► I choose to have joy today because:

► I am working towards my goal because:

My Plan A. is:

....

....

► The **first** thing I will do today to get me closer to achieving my Plan A. is:

Start Time: .... End Time: ....

► The **second** thing I will do today to get me closer to achieving my Plan A. is:

Start Time: .... End Time: ....

My next plan A is:

....

....

► The **first** thing I will do today to get me closer to achieving my next Plan A is:

Start Time: .... End Time: ....

► The **second** thing I will do today to get me closer to achieving my next Plan A is:

Start Time: .... End Time: ....

► Today, I will talk with/communicate with Mr./Ms./Dr. .... about:

EVENING REFLECTION

► The single most important thing I did today to get me closer to my goals was:

► The one thing that hurt my progress the most today was:

► I will overcome this obstacle tomorrow by:

5-DAY ACCOUNTABILITY CHECK

During the past 5 days...

► I made time for my success by:

► I increased my knowledge about:

► I asked for advice/guidance from:

....

....

....

► Over the next 5 days I will talk with/communicate
with Mr./Ms./Dr. .... about:

CONGRATULATIONS YOUNG MAN!

You have Successfully stuck to writing down and executing your goals for 66 days. Whatever your Plan A's are, you should have achieved them by now. If you haven't, that is okay too because you have made great progress towards reaching your Success. This journey was more about you developing the good habits of writing down your goals and working to achieve them daily. It was less about you actually reaching them. If you have learned how to write your plan down daily and work each day towards the Success you want and deserve, you have already been Successful. Continuing to do this will ensure that you reach any goal you set for yourself. You have developed Success as a habit.

Always remember that it is your job to Motivate, Inspire, and EMPOWER yourself to the Success you want and deserve.

Focused Thoughts & Notes

_____

_____

_____

_____

_____

_____

_____

_____

_____

_____

_____

_____

_____

_____

_____

_____

_____

_____

Focused Thoughts & Notes

Focused Thoughts & Notes

Focused Thoughts & Notes

Focused Thoughts & Notes

CPSIA information can be obtained
at www.ICGtesting.com
Printed in the USA
BVHW091923200521
607797BV00002B/172